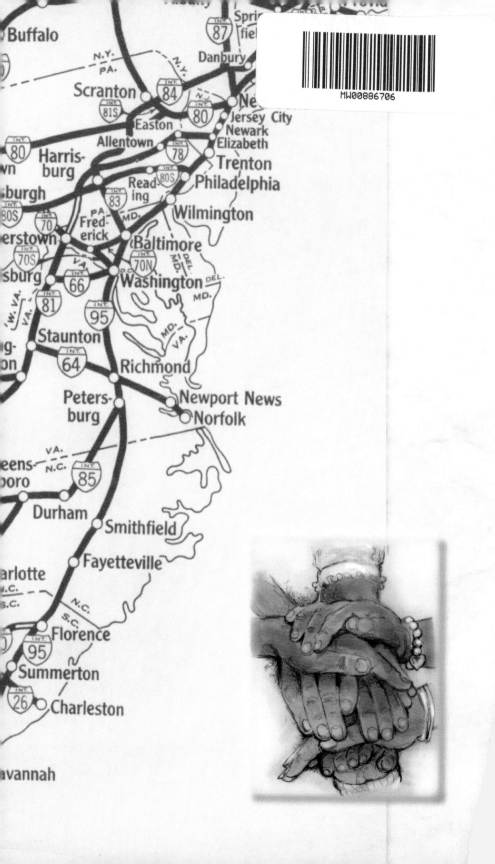

Buffalo

Springfield

INT 87

Danbury

N.Y. PA.

N.Y.

Scranton

INT 84

INT 81S

New

Easton

Jersey City

Allentown

Newark

INT 78

Elizabeth

Harrisburg

INT 80

Trenton

Reading

INT 80S

Philadelphia

PA.

INT 83

vn

sburg

INT 80S

INT 70

Frederick

MD.

Wilmington

erstown

INT 70S

Baltimore

MD.

DEL.

VA.

INT 70N

DEL.

sburg

INT 66

Washington

D.C.

MD.

W. VA.

VA.

INT 81

DEL.

MD.

gon

Staunton

MD. VA.

INT 64

Richmond

Petersburg

Newport News

Norfolk

VA.

eensboro

N.C.

INT 85

Durham

Smithfield

arlotte

N.C. S.C.

Fayetteville

N.C.

S.C.

INT 95

Florence

Summerton

INT 26

Charleston

avannah

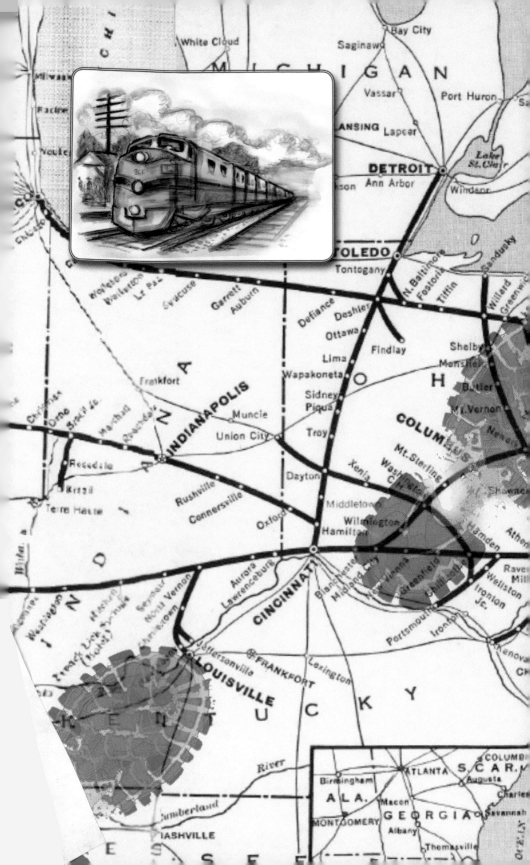

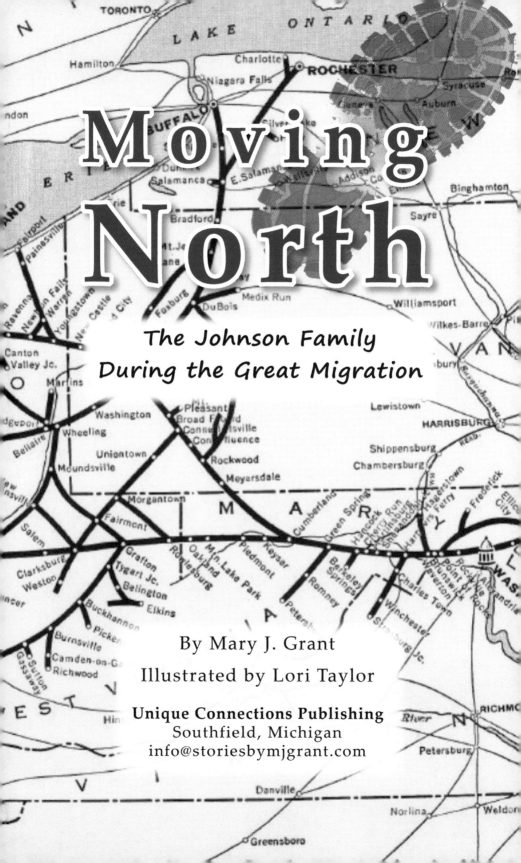

Moving North

The Johnson Family During the Great Migration

By Mary J. Grant

Illustrated by Lori Taylor

Unique Connections Publishing
Southfield, Michigan
info@storiesbymjgrant.com

CHAPTER 1
Leaving Home

Fred and his best friend Mr. Bell grew up in an environment of racial violence and poverty.

They often wondered what it would be like to move North. Their parents were Share Croppers and had an income of $250 to $300 a year. They decided to leave their low wage jobs at the Cotton Seed Mill, homes, friends, relatives and move to a new place.

On Friday evening, they took their money envelope, left their loving wives with money for their families and departed for their trip, while walking slowly, gazing back at their home. They put their thumbs out to hitchhike on Lynch Road, looking for a ride from a passing vehicle.

Fred said, "We are going a long way where there is no more Jim Crow."

Mr. Bell said, "Yes, Dayton, Ohio is about 740 miles."

Without giving it a second thought, Fred and Mr. Bell started down the highway. They walked until a 1947 Blue Ford Coupe pulled over.

A Colored man said, "You boys looking for a ride?"

"Yes," They said.

It was getting late and they were glad to get picked up before dark. Fred and Mr. Bell got into the back seat of the car. The driver turned on the radio to a blues station and began singing.

He said, "You can ride with me 'til we get to Memphis, Tennessee."

"Good!" said Mr. Bell.

It was a long trip, as they looked out the window at the farmland, cornfields, beans and all kinds of crops. After about 30 minutes they went to sleep.

"Wake up Fred, we are in Memphis, Tennessee," said Mr. Bell.

Fred woke up and stepped out of the car and said, "Thank you, kind sir."

Mr. Bell followed him, stretching his legs as he moved out of the car.

They walked to Mrs. Jones' house in the Colored section of Memphis. Mrs. Jones was Mr. Bell's cousin. They slept there that night and Mrs. Jones gave them some hot breakfast and packed food for the road. They tried to give Mrs. Jones some money, but she would not take it.

"No, No! Southern people gotta stick together," said Mrs. Jones.

They walked a long
way with their thumbs
out waiting for a car
or truck to stop. They
walked for about five
miles and finally a man
driving a flatbed truck
with two men riding on
the back stopped.

The man asked,
"Where are you going?"

Fred said, "We are
going to Dayton, Ohio."

The man said, "You can ride with me to Cincinnati, Ohio near the Ohio River."

Fred and Mr. Bell got on the flatbed truck with the two other men. Stored on the truck's flatbed was a load of hay, building material, and some lumber. The hay made a good seat and there was just enough space for the four men to sit. They got comfortable and went to sleep.

When they got to Cincinnati, they got out of the flatbed truck and saw the train depot. They walked to the train and hopped on the Northbound freight with some hoboes that had on torn clothes that smelled like farm animals.

The hoboes asked, "Where *y'all* going?"

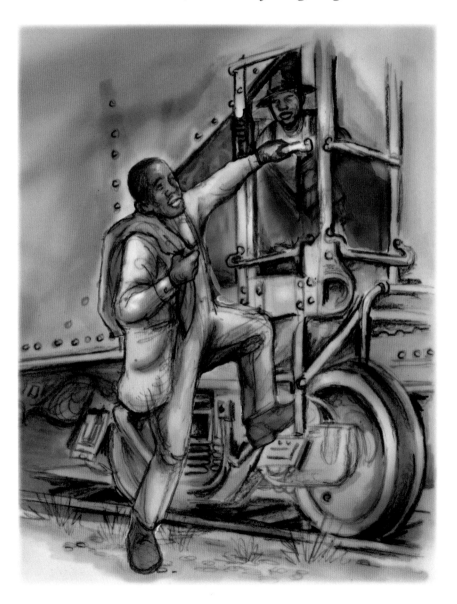

Mr. Bell said. "Fred and I are going to Dayton, Ohio to look for jobs."

Fred said, "We heard they are hiring a lot of people from the South in Dayton."

The hoboes turned away and looked like they had fallen asleep. Fred and Mr. Bell went to sleep too.

All of a sudden, they heard a loud scream, "Next stop Dayton, Ohio!"

Chapter 2
Finding a Job

They jumped off the train and looked for a payphone to call some relatives.

The relative came to pick them up near the train depot and drove them around town. While they were riding around, they saw a room for rent sign on Turner's Hat Shop window. They went in and asked for the room.

Mr. Turner showed them the room, they paid him and went to their room and fell asleep.

Later that day they went next door to the Germantown Grill Restaurant for some Soul Food in hopes of getting information on where to find work.

While in the restaurant, Fred met Claude White, a young man who was a World War II Navy Veteran. He told him he worked at GH&R Foundry, a factory that pours hot cast iron liquid into molds to make parts for machines, wheels for cars and trucks.

The next day Fred and Mr. Bell took the bus to GH&R Foundry.

When they arrived, there was a long line of Colored people from Kentucky, Tennessee, Georgia, Alabama, and Mississippi.

When Fred got to the front of the line, the personnel manager asked, "Hey boy, what is your name, where are you from and can you tell me something about yourself?"

Fred nervously said, "My name is Fred B. Johnson and I am from Jackson, Mississippi, I lived on 1621 Morehouse Street. My wife is Eliza Johnson and I have eight children ranging in ages eleven months to sixteen years old. My oldest daughter Cora died unexpectedly and that left two boys and five girls with each child being two or three years apart."

The personnel manager said, "You are tall and strong. This is a tough job. You are hired."

Mr. Bell was hired also.

When Fred started working, he tried hard to do well and his boss said he was doing a good job. The foundry was dusty, hot, dangerous and dirty with grimy soot covering everything. People talked a lot about life, but they kept up with their work. Three lines were moving, line one was a fast line with iron, line two was the molder's line where Fred poured liquid iron and line three was the shakeout of the iron.

It was very hot, about 150 degrees and the men would sit down every half hour to cool off. When the whistle blew, they rushed out the door to go home. Fred and Mr. Bell always removed their dirty work clothes before leaving for home.

Chapter 3

Getting Ready to Bring the Family

On Friday, Fred went to the GH&R Foundry Credit Union to get a loan. The manager interviewed him and he asked for a five hundred dollars loan.

She said, "Come back on Monday for your answer."

On Monday the Credit Union Manager said, "Sorry sir, you need a co-signer because you might leave any day and go back to Mississippi." Fred asked, "What is a co-signer?"

She said, "A co-signer is a person who is responsible for the loan if it is not paid."

He went to his friends and asked would they help him and they all said no. When the work whistle blew, he waited for Whitey. Whitey was Claude's nickname.

Fred was almost in tears and wondered who could he get to co-sign.

Fred asked, "Whitey, can you loan me five hundred dollars?"

Whitey said, "Man, I don't have that kind of money."

Fred asked, "Can you co-sign for my loan?"

Whitey stopped walking and paused, put his hand on his chin and said, "What are you going to do with that kind of money Freddie B?"

Freddie B. was Fred's nickname.

Freddie B. said, "I want to pay for my family's train tickets and build a house for my family. In Mississippi, I did all kinds of carpentry, cement and brickwork."

Whitey said, "Because I am a veteran, I have good credit, I will co-sign for the loan. But you must pay the credit union back on time."

Freddie B. and Whitey went inside the GH&R Credit Union and both signed the loan agreement for five hundred dollars.

Freddie B. had a big smile on his face and clapped his hands as he waited at the bus stop for the Germantown bus. He was going to look for some land to build a house for his family.

Fred pulled the cord for the Dennison stop and got off the bus. He walked down Germantown to Dennison and turned on Richley Street where he met a hog farmer named Jake Bennet, the owner of the land.

Jake Bennet said, "Come across the street and see my farm."

Fred walked around the farm and saw the hogs, horses and chicken coops.

Fred looked closely at the piglets and asked,

"Can I buy these two piglets? When they are grown, they will be sows and I can make money when they reproduce."

Jake said, "Yes, you can leave your piglets here, just help feed them."

Fred counted his money for the land and the two piglets and handed it to Jake.

Jake gave him a deed for 1915 Richley and Fred put his mark on the line.

Fred was overjoyed when he realized what had just happened.

He said, "I have to register my deed for the property with the city clerk and I own two piglets."

"Yes!" said Jake Bennet.

He sat on a big rock on his property and said,
"I am so excited because I am going to build my
family's new home."

A neighbor named Jethro Nelson came over and told Fred that this area is sometimes called Hogbottom because of the farm across the street. They laughed and talked all evening about how they were going to build their houses on the land they owned, their hometowns and as the sunset Jethro went to his house.

Fred shouted, "See you later neighbor!"

Chapter 4
New Beginnings

Fred walked back from the bus stop to go to his room at Turner's Hat Shop. He stopped by the Germantown Grill to eat dinner. He saw Whitey and they shared their experiences of the day. That night he could hardly sleep for thinking of all the opportunities of the future.

That next day at work he could hardly focus on his job. At the end of the week, he found a telephone booth to call Mississippi to talk with his wife and children.

"Daddy is on the telephone." Mother said.

The family gathered around the phone in the front room.

Daddy said, "Get ready to move North because I have purchased some land to build a house for our family. Once the house is ready, I will send train tickets for you all to join me in Dayton, Ohio in a few months."

The family began to celebrate by jumping up, down and sharing happy hugs. All the children were very happy because they thought they could do better in the North. There would be better schools, jobs, Colored people would be treated fairly.

Daddy said, "I can't wait to see the family at the train station and tell the children I love them."

Mother slowly hung the phone up and finished cooking.

After two months, the tickets
came in the mail and the family
began to pack suitcases, pillowcases
and a bedsheet. On the day before
the trip, Mother prepared the food
for the train ride. She selected fruit, boiled eggs,
fried chicken, thick sliced ham, yellow pound cake,
two loaves of bread and salt in a handkerchief for
the food. The food was wrapped in wax paper,
organized and placed in shoeboxes. The family was
so excited they could hardly sleep that night.

Chapter 5
Family on the Move

The next day, the family was all dressed and ready to travel to the North. Before the family left, they all stood in a circle with their heads bowed as Mother prayed.

Floyd asked, "Why is everyone so sad?"

Mothers said, "We are moving!"

Gloria asked, "Where?"

Mother said, "North to a better life."

Earnestine asked, "Where is Alfred?"

Mother said, "He left last month on the train to stay with cousins so he could help your Father get the house ready in Dayton, Ohio."

When the family arrived at the train station in Jackson, Mississippi, it was crowded with families talking about going north. The family looked for the train that had B&O Railroad.

The Train Conductor screamed, "All aboard!"

In the Jim Crow South, Colored people had to sit in the back of the train. The families lined up and waited to sit down.

Mother said, "Gloria, take baby Maymay, her bottles of milk, food and diaper bag."

The family always called the baby Maymay, a name of Mother's good friend, but her real name is Mary.

Mother lugged the big knotted bed sheet, Floyd carried the jammed packed suitcase, Earnestine tugged the crammed pillow case and Jewel carried the yummy smelling shoe boxes of food.

Gloria asked, "Where is Nancy?"

Mother said, "Nancy is in Meridian, Mississippi at Grandma Nancy's house and she will be coming later."

The people quickly filled up the train. There were people with suitcases tied together with belts, things in crock-a-sacks and big bags of all kinds of food.

There were no racks for luggage in the Colored car.

The Colored coach attendants said, "Put all your things near your feet out of the walkway!"

The people had to stuff everything close to their feet. It was very uncomfortable.

Jewel asked, "Can I go to the toilet in the front of the railroad car?"

"No, that is the White people's toilet and you can get in big trouble!" said Mother.

The conductor yelled, "All aboard!"

Chapter 6
The Train Ride

The doors slammed and the train's whistle blew as the train vibrated down the tracks. The family looked out the window as the houses got smaller. Farmland appeared with barns, horses, cows, rows of corn, and green beans.

The family became very quiet with tears and sad faces; they were upset because they were leaving family, friends and relatives.

Mother said, "Hold your heads up for we are going to encounter many different kinds of experiences and meet new friends."

Mother started humming her favorite song, *"His Eye is on the Sparrow."*

The train started moving faster, sparks started flashing as the train moved over the tracks. The constant movement of the train put the family to sleep. The baby started to cry.

Everyone said, "Shhhh!"

Gloria said, "Oops, Maymay wet on me!"

She changed the baby's diaper and rocked her to sleep.

The family traveled to Memphis, Tennessee where the people were waiting. The families got off the train to use the Colored only restroom. The families returned to the crowded train as the new families entered. The Colored coach attendant moved around making sure they had everything tucked tightly around their feet.

The conductor shouted, "All Aboard, next stop Paducah, Kentucky, the Mason-Dixon Line!"

When the train stopped, everyone got out and stretched their arms, legs and used the toilet.

Floyd said, "We have crossed the Mason-Dixon Line and now we can sit anywhere we want."

Earnestine said, "We don't have to sit in the back of the train any longer, no more Jim Crow laws."

"All Aboard!" yelled the conductor, "Next stop Dayton, Ohio!"

The families all took a different seat and put their luggage and other things on the rack above their seats. They settled down and enjoyed looking at the farms and all the beautiful scenery.

Before they knew it, a big sign said Perry and Sixth Street.

The conductor called out, "Dayton, Ohio Union Station!"

The families got excited as they lined up to get off the train.

Mother said, "Come children, let's stay together." The Johnson family all walked to the sidewalk near the street to wait for their father.

The children said, "Let's take a Yellow Cab."

Mother said, "No, your Father said he was coming."

So, the family sat on the bench and waited and waited and waited. Their Father did not come. After an hour everyone was gone from the train station, so Mother hailed a cab.

The man in the cab said, "Where to ma'am?"

Mother stopped to think, whether to wait for the next train back to Mississippi or go where she thought the house was located.

Mother said, "Take us to Dennison and Richley on the Westside of Dayton".

The cab driver drove to Dennison and looked for the house.

Mother said, "Just drive until you see Richley."

The cab driver asked, "What should I do when we get to Richley?"

Mother said, "Just turn right."

When the cab driver got to Richley he turned right and drove until he got to the creek.

Mother said, "Turn around and drive the other way on Richley."

The cab driver drove until he stopped at the Dennison street sign.

Chapter 7
Home

When the family arrived on Dennison and Richley Street, their Father was sitting on a big rock. They forgot all about waiting and was glad to see him.

Mother said, "Freddie B. Johnson, do you know how glad we are to see you?"

Father paid the cab driver and went back to see the family. He picked up the baby and kissed her on the cheek.

Daddy said, "I am glad to see you too, but I had to work overtime and was unable to pick you up. When I went to the train station no one was there, so I came here."

The family started walking around. They started walking through some wild tall grass and saw the house.

When they got in the house Alfred, their brother, was sitting in a big chair. He was glad to see the family. Daddy and Mother hugged and then all the family hugged.

Daddy said, "I missed all of you."

Mother said, "We all missed you too!"

Daddy had a sad look on his face and said, "I put the cinder blocks, walls up with windows and curtains, but I needed a few more days to get the water turned on."

Floyd said, "You mean we have to tote water!"

"Yes!" said Daddy.

The next day, Mother was busy cooking on the pot belly stove with some food on the cooktop and the biscuits baking in the hot drawer. The family awoke to the smell of a wonderful breakfast of sausage, grits, bacon, eggs and buttered biscuits with a can of Karo syrup.

The family bowed their heads, gave thanks and ate their breakfast.

Daddy said, "Thank you God for bringing my family safely to me."

Mother said, "We are thankful for our new home."

They all smiled as the family enjoyed the delicious breakfast prepared by Mother.

The next day, Daddy and Alfred cut the front yard and started digging trenches to the sewage city water line on Richley street.

Daddy said, "Floyd I need you to make a scale blueprint drawing of this house."

Floyd started measuring the interior and exterior dimensions of the rooms, walls, doors and windows. Floyd sketched a scaled rough outline drawing of a floor plan.

Daddy said, "Make sure you are taking accurate measurements."

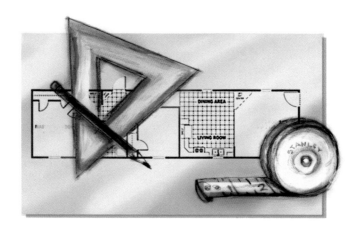

Floyd worked hard using the measuring tape and a triangular scale ruler on graph paper to complete the blueprint.

Floyd said, "Daddy come and look!"

Floyd laid the scaled drawing out on the floor to show his Father how he marked everything in place with the one-fourth inch (1/4") equals one-inch (1") scale.

Daddy asked, "Did you measure all the rooms, closets and hallways?"

Floyd said, "Yes! This is a special blueprint to take to the city of Dayton's water and sewage architects for a permit."

Daddy said, "I am so proud of you son."

Floyd and his Father took the blueprint to Dayton Blueprint Company to get the required six copies for the city. They took the finished product to Mr. Bean's office at the City of Dayton Sewage Department.

Mr. Bean said, "Make sure you put the permit on the house to show that the digging has been approved."

When they returned home, they put the permit on the house and started digging the next day. They worked hard most of the evening and half the night. By the end of the week the waterline was fixed and the toilet was ready with running water throughout the entire house. Floyd was really proud because when he returns to school in the fall, he would be a fifth-grader.

Chapter 8
Now Let's Celebrate

Labor Day was a great celebration for families. The Nelsons and many other families came to welcome the Johnson family to the neighborhood.

Dorothy and Stanford, the new neighbors, talked about the close community of families that moved from the South and found it difficult to move in many areas in Dayton.

Alfred said, "Look down the street near the hill there is Jake Bennet' hog farm. Many times, the children in the neighborhood would go down the hill to watch the hogs eat old leftover slop and listen to their funny noises."

The children went
over to the farm and
had fun watching the
chickens walking up and
down their ladders in the

chicken coop and the horses
running around inside the fence.

Later that day, the children
went for a walk on the narrow
trails near the trailers and the
boxcar homes.

As they walked back home, Earnestine asked, "Where is that the smell coming from?"

Alfred replied, "That smell is coming from the water treatment plant on Nicholas Road and Danner. They take water from the river and clean it for the people of Montgomery County to drink."

"Wow," said Gloria, "I'm thirsty."

The new friends told the names of the high schools to attend — Roosevelt and Dunbar and Elementary Schools were Wogamen and soon to be built, Miami Chapel. They also shared information that would help make the transition to Dayton a successful experience.

They told them how they rode the bus downtown and shopped at Rikes' Department Store or the Arcade which led to the back entrance of Kresge's 5 & 10 cents store.

On holidays, the families always wanted to go to Lakeside Amusement Park with roller coaster, ferris wheels, bumpers cars, tilt-a-whirls, food to eat and lots of fun.

That night the family was very happy because they felt they had come to a good place on the west side of Dayton. They all sat around sharing food and eating all kinds of desserts.

Eliza said, "Come and get some of my Eliza's Tea Cakes fresh from the hot drawer."

All you could hear was the adults saying, "Those Tea Cakes are sooo delicious!"

But the children said "Mmmmmmm good!"

ELIZA'S TEA CAKES

2 1/2 cups sifted all-purpose flour

1/4 tsp salt

2 tsp baking powder

1 tsp nutmeg

1 tsp cinnamon

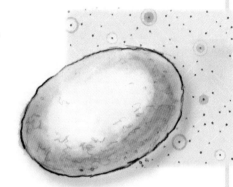

1/2 cup butter

1 cup sugar

2 beaten eggs

1/2 tsp pure vanilla extract (May use lemon or almond extract)

1 tbsp milk (evaporated milk or buttermilk)

Sift flour, salt, baking powder nutmeg, cinnamon together. In a separate bowl cream sugar, butter and add eggs to the mixture add vanilla and milk mix well. Add dry ingredients to creamed butter, sugar, egg, milk and vanilla mixture. Blend well. Place dough on lightly floured board (or countertop). Sprinkle a little flour over the dough and roll out to about 1/2 inch thick. Cut dough with flour dipped cookie cutter or a jar/glass. Place on a flat cooking pan. Bake at 350 degrees for 12 to 15 minutes.

AFTERWORDS

The Johnson Family moving North in the Great Migration was one of the greatest ideas Fred Johnson had because it taught many lessons of courage, perseverance, resilience and faith in their pursuit of living the American Dream. The inspiring vision of never giving up on chasing goals and seeking improved conditions was a life lesson.

The families that lived on the West Side of Dayton, which was sometimes called Hogbottom, will always be remembered.

Dayton was unprepared for its rapid expansion during the African American Great Migration and housing growth was a problem. Many families moved wherever they could find inexpensive land or homes. Some families chose this southwestern community of Dayton because it was underdeveloped land near a hog farm. The families were a melting pot of valued productive citizens who were all looking for meaningful opportunities for their families.

As time passed, segregation forced integration and the communities began to change. The Black community moved and their businesses that once thrived were shuttered. The community was renamed by two African American land developers named William Leigh and C. J. McLin Jr. to Madden Hills and they relocated Dunbar High School from its Summit Street address to Jake Bennet's farm known as Hogbottom. The community still has working-class people trying hard to keep their community together.

The offsprings of the Hogbottom Community have generations after generation contributed to Ohio's communities and the United States and the World.

African Americans are still fighting for their freedom, even after the civil rights movement. The struggle continues with each new generation growing stronger with the residual movement in their hearts while remembering their ancestors' pride.

To the Promise Land of
The GREAT MIGRATION - 1916-1970*

by Freida Wesson Bosh

It all began in the 20th century,
There were problems for African Americans,
And the Great Migration is when it first began.

The Southern States practiced discrimination and racial segregation,
That was unfair treatment against the African Americans.

Used "Plessy vs Ferguson" to prove their case,
That legislative decision of "separate but equal" was ruled.

Each Southern state was governed by Jim Crow laws,
Promoting poor economic conditions and unfair wages.

That's why six million African Americas participated in the great move,
From Southern states practicing racial segregation.

The Great Migration promised the African Americans success,
Of many economic opportunities and higher salaries.

But the price they paid for freedom to an unknown place,
Was worth the risks of traveling to a new Northern land.

The challenge of racism wounded the Northern pride,
But the African American will always require freedom and justice
to survive.

* dates from Great Migration (African American) - Wikipedia

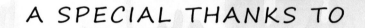

A SPECIAL THANKS TO

My family members - Jewel Johnson Jones, Nancy Johnson Mayes, Floyd Johnson and the deceased family members – Alfred Johnson, Cora Johnson, Gloria Wesson and Earnestine Smith.

I appreciate all those people who supported me on my journey of writing this book.

Claude "Whitey" White, Denise Whatley, Frieda Bosh, Marcella Norton Ashe, Dorothy Nelson Power and Gloria Nelson Daniel.

MJG

Some of the Families from Hogbottom

The Johnson family and others created enjoyable memories as they faced the challenges and opportunities of their everyday life.

Below are the names of families that shared memories as they faced the challenges and opportunities of their everyday life during the Great Migration.

Thomas, Latimer, Crowder, Camp, Willis, Bennet, Henderson, Mitchel, Botman, Norton, Nelson, Ross, McKee, Broadus, Roger, Stone, Dillard, Jones, Melon, Stone, Burk, Brown, Rice, Hill, Brown, Reynold, Roger, Clay and Johnson.

Some of the landmarks in the neighborhood:

Daddy-O's, Bennet Store, Dump Yard, Scrap Metal & Iron Yard, Brazil Lane Apartments, Mitchell Store, Ren's Market and W&J Store.

Author Bio

Mary J. Grant is an author, educator, storyteller and workshop presenter who has devoted her career to educating children. As a teacher, supervisor and administrator, she always reminded her students that knowledge is power. Reading, writing and learning have always been her passion and a significant part of her life.

She is the author of four books: *My Daddy Taught Me To Read, Floyd B's Pond, Shadows on Sunday and My Special Jar*. Each book has Maymay as its main character and the members of her family are supporting characters.

She is a professional storyteller and has told engaging stories to adults and children all over the United States.

Mary J. Grant - Author/Storyteller/educator/workshop presenter
Website: www.storiesbymjgrant.com
Email: marygrant1915@gmail.com

Illustrator Bio

Lori Taylor is a Michigan children's author and illustrator and artist. She has been writing, drawing, and telling stories ever since she was a child growing up in Clarkston, in a once wild northern Oakland County.

She has been artist-in-residence for the Sleeping Bear Dunes National Lakeshore, Porcupine Mountains Wilderness State Park, and Literacy Legacy Fund of Michigan.

She is the author and illustrator of her Michigan Holly Wild series, picture books and her Sense-of-Place Storyteller series of Michigan legends. Lori lives and works in the Manistee National Forest with her many pets and the wild animals outside her studio door.

Lori Taylor - Artist/Author/Illustrator
Website: www.loritaylorart.com

Cataloging-in-Publication Data
Name: Grant, Mary J., Author
Taylor, Lori, Illustrator

Title: Moving North: The Johnson Family
During the Great Migration

Description: Unique Connections Publishing Co.,
Southfield, MI 48033, 2020
Summary: A story of detailed true experiences
of the Johnson family leaving their home in the South
during the Great Migration and creating a new life in
the North while overcoming many of life's challenges.

Identifiers: 1st U.S. Edition | (softcover) |
First Printing, August 2020
Subjects: CYAC: African American—history.
|Great Migration—history. | Family—history.
| Non-fiction. |

ISBN: 978-1-7352923-0-4
ISBN: 978-1-7352923-1-1 Ebook
LCCN: 2020913226

Published in the U.S.A., August 2020
By Unique Connections Publishing Co.
DiggyPOD
Printed in the United States

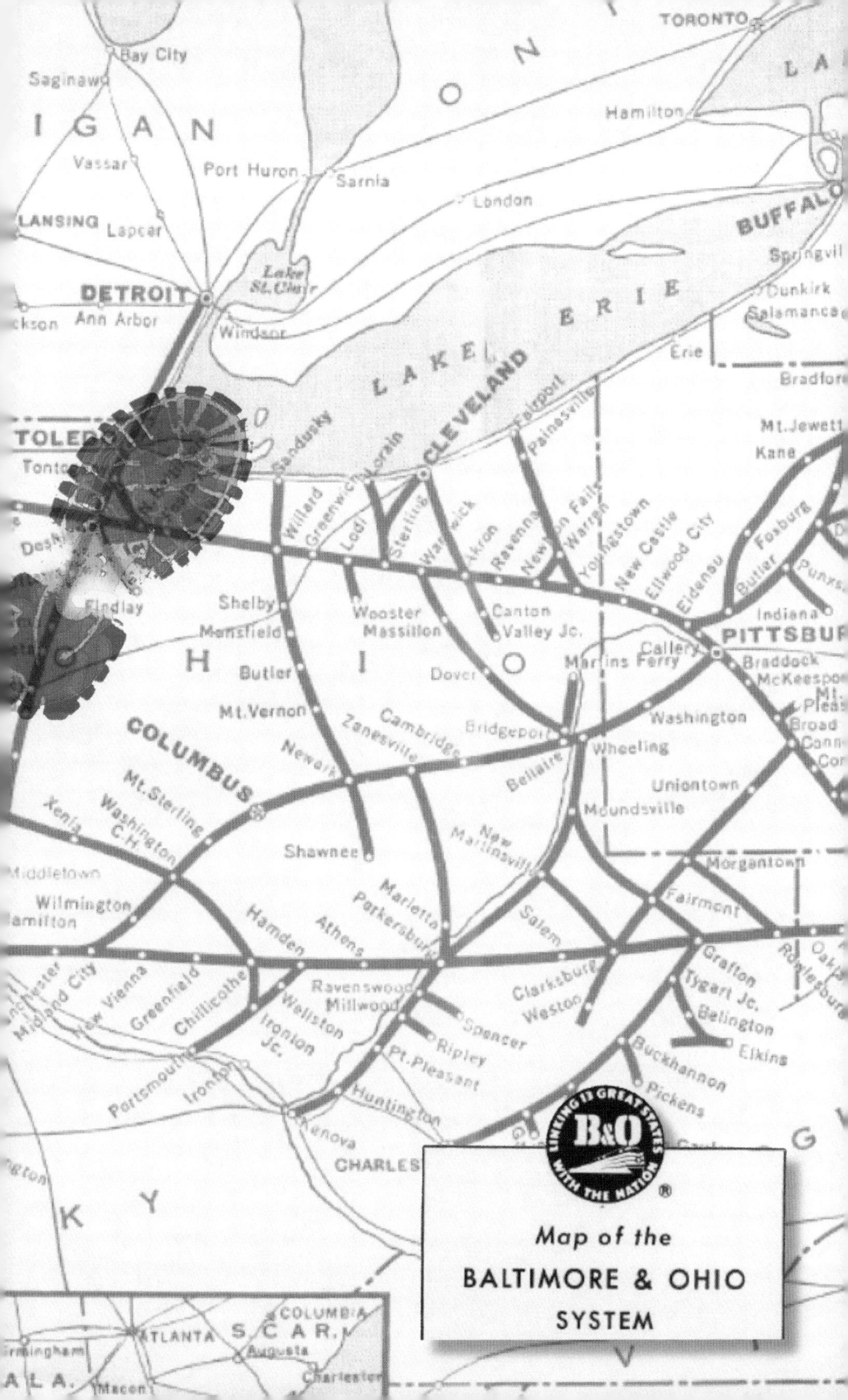

Map of the

BALTIMORE & OHIO SYSTEM

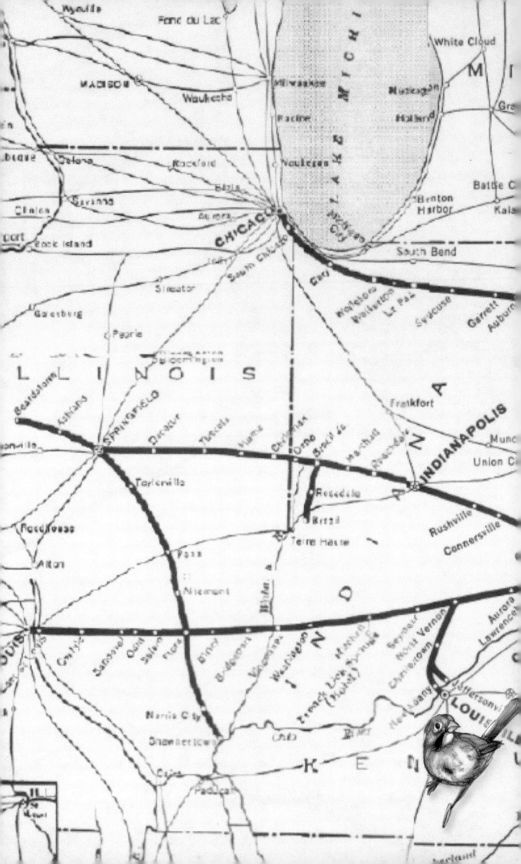